GATESHEAD REVISITED

by

Professor Adrian Swall
Curator
Bensham Museum of Antiquities.

A WARD ENNIS PUBLICATION

First published in 1990
in the
United Kingdom
by
Ward Ennis Publications

ISBN 0 9515405 1 3

Illustrations
by
Peter Millen

Published and Printed
by
Ward Ennis Publications
3 Earsdon Road, Monkseaton
Whitley Bay, Tyne & Wear
NE25 9SX

Preface

Last summer I undertook a sponsored plodge of the Northumberland coast, in aid of Museum funds. This enterprise was to prove doubly beneficial. In the first place enough money was raised to cover my winter lecture tour of the Caribbean. Secondly, whilst resting at Bamburgh, an important discovery was made.

Jellyfish having made the foreshore unplodgeable, I visited the Castle, whilst waiting for conditions to improve. The concierge (Norman for 'watchie') invited me to examine the archives. Whilst most of the material was familiar, I was surprised to find a bundle of papers, previously overlooked. Permission was requested, and granted, for their removal to the Museum for further analysis.

The jellyfish soon departed, and the fund-raising resumed.

Back in the Museum, the papers provided a valuable breakthrough in filling a gap in our knowledge of our forebears. The writings were the life's work of the first Custodian of the Castle.

At the request of William the Conqueror, he had forsaken his native Gascony to take on the task of managing the Castle. In the long winter months, when tourism was at its quietest, he would read the works of the local authors and poets. His knowledge of the North East became encyclopedic, and in order to spread this among the natives, he introduced the general knowledge quiz into the Lord Crewe and Castle Hotel in the village. The Mizen Head and Victoria were invited to join a league, organised by the Custodian. The popularity of these events spread quickly throughout the area, and their inventor became known as Bamburgh Gascoigne.

The following pages describe life on Tyneside, as researched by the famous quizmaster. They represent an important contribution to our knowledge of the area 900 years ago.

Professor Adrian Swall
Curator
Bensham Museum of Antiquities.

For the benefit of those readers who are not conversant with Latin, the inscriptions on the front cover translate as follows:

TOP

HIC, BAMBVRGI LOCUM WILLELMVS EXPET IT

'Here, William covets a place at Bamburgh'

MIDDLE

HIC, HAROLD REX INTERFECTVS EST

'Here, King Harold is wounded'

BOTTOM

IN POTESTATEM NORMANNORVM
REDACTVM GATESHEAD FLORET

'Gateshead flourishes under Norman rule'

SPECTACVLVM FLORIS
'Garden Festival'

CHAPTER 1

Mattie, Masie & Proggie Mats

When Mattie Hall started work at Redheugh Pit it was 1045 – A.D. that is, not A.M. He had left Windmill Hill school on the third Friday in July; now on the fourth Monday, he was ready, bait-tin in hand, for work. His parents were divided on his chosen career. His mother, Peggie, wanted him to further his education at the College in Durham Road. This establishment had a world-wide reputation as a centre of excellence for the Sciences, as well as the Arts. Albert, his father, on the other hand, could see no reason why Mattie should not follow his seven brothers into a career in the pit. And he prevailed. After all, his coal merchant's business owed its existence to the free coal allocation given to his sons, all of whom lived in the family home in Askew Road. Another free source of raw materials would mean even better year-end results. And that was more important than having a scholar in the family.

So, the pit it was. And Mattie, at 16, was more interested in girls than in further education. He had heard about the young ladies who served in the pit canteen, and spent their wages on Saturday night in the Miners Welfare. Culture, he had decided, would have to wait.

As was the custom, he worked a week lying on, and was paid for the first time at the end of the second week. His work involved drawing trucks through the workings which were too small for the pit ponies. This was very dangerous and to overcome his fear, he would sing the old mining songs of the time. '16 Bushels' would echo through the galleries and shafts as he made his way on hands and knees through the damp, dusty tunnels. This did not go unnoticed, as he was quickly invited to enter the Welfare talent contest on the day after pay-day.

He was drawn second, after an old man who tore the Evening Chronicle into pieces, which eventually took the shape of a dozen pigeons, wingtip to wingtip. He left to a storm of boos. Nervously, Mattie took the stage clutching his lute.

"On a coont o' fower" he instructed the drummer, cazooist and the man on the spoons.

"Some people say a man is made oot o' mud" he began, as the canteen girls in the front row jumped up and began dancing in the aisle. Before he finished, the whole audience had joined in, dancing and singing. They might as well have ended the contest there and then. The magician's rabbit was chased from the hall by the Concert chairman's whippet, whilst it was still in the magician's hat. The comedian fared no better.

"Did ye hear the one aboot the dyslexic atheist? 'E spent aal 'e's life denyin' the existence iv any form iv dog!" (Boo, hiss, gerroff, etc.....)

The treasurer went around with the domino card, as the judges deliberated. The Concert chairman cleared his throat as he stood up to speak.

"The neet's winna, ladies an' gentlemen, is the dynamic vocalist, Mattie Haall an' he wins the forst prize o' twenty free pint vouchas. Howay, son" he added beckoning Mattie forward, "its noo yor duty to draa the domino to see who's won the domino card."

Mattie drew the 6-3 from the velvet bag, and the treasurer tore the brown paper strip from the card.

"Siventeen!" shouted the treasurer. "Maisie R".

Maisie Robinson, apprentice soup-ladler in the pit canteen, had won the last card of the night, and picked her way through the tables to the stage.

The treasurer handed the half-crown prize to Mattie, for him to present. He duly handed it to Maisie, and shook her hand.

"Wot's the marra, son?" asked the Concert chairman. "Are ye not ganna hoy the lips on 'hor?"

Mattie closed his eyes and tentatively kissed Maisie on the cheek. This brought great applause from the audience, as he out- blushed Maisie. Kissing behind the Art Gallery was one thing, but on stage in the Welfare was something he wasn't quite ready for. Quickly regaining his composure, he led her from the stage back to his table.

"Will yi help iz git rid o' some o' these vouchas, Maisie?" he asked.

"Aal reet" she replied smiling "but nee slavva, mind! Aa'll just gan and git me handbag."

She returned with six of the canteen ladies, who quickly used up the remains of his prize.

"Last ordas!" shouted Joe Robertson, the barman, as Mattie plucked up the courage to ask Maisie if he could take her home. She agreed. So long as he escorted her friends as well. Something to do with solidarity. He couldn't say "no".

The first gooseberry lived on West Street, and the second on Sunderland Road. Three and four lived in Old Fold, which was then the Latin quarter of Gateshead. The last two lived up the hill in well-heeled, sophisticated Deckham. It was well known that the residents frowned upon late night revellers, and had been known to pour the dregs of their wine bottles from their drawing room windows onto the heads of those who disturbed their peace. So the girls tiptoed through the streets to their basement flat in the west wing of Deckham Towers. Mattie slunk along behind, feeling a little uncomfortable in these wealthy surroundings. The girls swung open the gates to the Towers and swung them closed again, with Mattie on the outside.

"D'ye fancy gannin oot wirriz next week?" he asked Maisie, through the bars.

"Wheriboots?" she replied.

"Worriboot the dance at the Two Bridges?"

"Aye, aal reet: Thorsday neet isn't it?"

"Aye: see ye Thorsday!"

"If this is bein' grown-up" Mattie told himself, "Aa'm aal forrit!" And he made his way home, exchanging pleasantries with the various stragglers encountered en route.

Mattie arrived home as his mother was putting the cat out.

"Sittin ower close to the fire was she?" he asked as the cat was doused with a bucket of water.

....residents frowned on late night revellers....

"Aye, son, that's one mair life she's used up. How did the contest gan?"

"Aa cum forst, and the audience gave iz a standin' ovashin!"

"Well, stick it in the cubbad under the stairs, till we decide wot to dee wirrit."

Mattie quickly fell into a steady pattern of pitwork, courting Maisie and winning the Welfare talent contest. The committee eventually gave him his own spot on Saturday nights, paying him a crown for his trouble. Steadily his repertoire grew to include such classics as 'Wotcheer Mary Lou', 'Waalk Reet Back', 'Will Ye Still Luv Iz the Morra' and 'Rubba Baal'.

One night, as he walked Maisie home, he confided his ambition to her.

"When Aa git a bit owlder, Aa'd like t' buy one of them big toon-hooses on Whitehaal Road. Y'knaa like the one belangin' to the rich timba morchint."

"The one wi' the broon cortins upstairs?"

"Aye – Aa'm ganna save aal me croons worra git for singing and gan on neet-shift till Aa've ornt inuff for a deposit."

"But ye'll need thoosinds; it'll take ages to dee that on yor own. Two cud dee it twice as quick."

"That soonds like a proposal to me, like."

"Well, worriboorrit? Aa cud git a paper roond."

"Aye, aal reet; but divvent tell neebody mind. If me faatha finds oot, Aa'll git wrang. Nen o' me brothas is married, and the aadest's thorty fower. Anyway, when Aa'm twenty one, Aa can please meesel. Worriboot ye?"

"Just the same – until Aa'm twenty one Aa've gorra dee worram telt."

"Reet, then, that gives us five years to save up."

In 1050, the wedding was arranged at the Registry Office in Walker Terrace, for the first Saturday after Pancake Tuesday.

Mattie called at the Registry Office on the Tuesday to arrange the licence. Byronclough, the Teesside poet was standing in reception.

"Noo there, Mattie; Aa didn't knaa ye wor a poet", said Byronclough.

"Aa'm not", replied Mattie "Aa'm efta a marriage licence."

"Well, ye'd berra stand in that queue ower there; this queue's for poetic licence."

Mattie completed the formalities and returned home.

"So yor gannin aheed wirrit, are ye?" stormed Albert. "Efta aal Aa've telt ye. Aal wimmin's witches, son. They'll just use ye, and when they're finished wi'ye, they'll hoy ye away like an empty chip packet."

"Aa divvent care wot ye say, faatha, Aa've aalready bowt a hoose."

And so they were wed. For ten years they strove to bring up their sons Jackie and Harry and to keep up their mortgage payments. To supplement her income, Maisie ran a chain-mail- order catalogue. Mattie continued to work underground and sing at weekends. He was booked in the Miners' Welfares as far afield as Ashington and Horden.

It was on a Gala Night appearance at Horden that disaster struck. In his grand finale, 'Me Who's Got Nowt', the climax was cut short by a sudden coughing fit. The audience was stunned as he was helped gasping from the stage.

On Monday morning the pit doctor tapped Mattie's chest and frowned.

"Breathe in. Noo oot," he instructed. "Aa thowt see. Aa'm sorry, son, but it luks like ye've got moconiosis."
(Pneumoconiosis had not yet been discovered).

"Not the dust?" sighed Mattie. "Worriboot me singing?"

"It's ya job ye shud be worryin aboot, son, not ya singin," warned the doctor.

"Ye've worked ya last shift undagroond!"

"Worram Aa ganna dee?"

"Why not apply for the job wi' the pit pony dressage team?"

"Aa'd feel a reet Jessie gannin roond wi aal them posh claes on."

"Ye shud knaa sorfiss jobs is kept for the Union officials. Why not apply for orly retirement?"

"Aa'm ownly thorty-one, man. Aa cudn't just retire."

"Divvent fret, son, ye'll find summik. If ye want my advice ye'll move to the coast and git yassel plenty fresh air."

Maisie and the boys were philosophical about the news.

"If that's wot the doctor says, Mattie, that's wot we'll dee, won't wi, lads?", she said.

"Aye faatha," agreed eight year old Jackie, "we can gan plodgin any time we like."

"An' huntin for willicks an' aal," added Harry, who was a year younger.

The Whitehall Road town house was put up for sale, and a semi on the front at Whitley Bay, bought.

After the move, Mattie struggled for months to come to terms with his enforced idleness. No heavy work, no singing! What would he do?

"Why not take up carpentry?" suggested Maisie.

"Nar, the doctor says Aa shudn't fret."

"Worriboot collectin' stamps?"

"Nee gud: last time Aa started, Aa coughed aal ower them and they blew away oot the winda."

"Well, while ye make ya mind up, giz a hand with this proggie mat."

"Worrizit?"

"It's for wor Polly's front room."

"Aa knaa, but it's aal porple – why divvent ye add a pattan or summik."

"Aal reet, clivver dick, if ye knaa aal aboorrit, ye make it."

So he did. Cutting up an old yellow drape from his stage wardrobe, he progged in a canary, the symbol of Redheugh Pit. At last, he had stumbled upon a pastime that would fill the empty hours. As he progged in the tip of the canary's tail, who should walk in but Alf Robbins, his old boss from the pit.

"Wot cheer, Alf, howyiganninon?" asked Mattie.

"Canny man, how's yassel?" replied Alf.

"Strugglin to make ends meet."

"Well, Aa hope this'll be some use to ye – the lad's had a whip-roond and sponsored willick-sexin' : there's aboot 50 croons here," he said, handing Mattie a bag of money. He was taken aback. This was totally unexpected and he was stuck for words.

Alf, feeling awkward, changed the subject.

"Wot's this here, Mattie," he asked pointing to the proggie mat "a Chinese spuggie?"

"Nar, it's the Redheugh emblem, a canary!"

"That wud luk smashin' in the foya o' the Pit offices. How much d'ye want forrit?"

"Aa hevvint thowt...."

"Aa'll give ye thorty bob. Howay noo, that's fair isn't it?"

"Aye, aal reet, gannon then," agreed Mattie.

Maisie was not pleased when she discovered that Polly's mat had disappeared. Mattie was instructed to prepare a replacement. This time he made a landscape, 'The Haywain on Windmill Hills'. He became so engrossed in his hobby that Maisie had to lock all of the wardrobes and linen cupboards in case they were raided for raw materials. Eventually, the house was full of mats: large, small, square, round, plain and patterned. Maisie became fed up with tripping over them, and the fact that Mattie's efforts were better than her own.

"D'ye not think it's time ye got shot of aal these?" she protested.

"Why nar," replied Mattie indignantly. "Aa like hevin summik to luk at."

"Aa thowt ye'd hev sellt some o' them by noo. The money'd come in handy, wot wi' the bairn's school uniforms to buy."

"Aa tell ye wot," compromised Mattie, Aa'll keep me favourites and take the rest doon to the Quayside on Sunda. Ye nivva knaa, Aa might orn a few croons."

As a newcomer to the Quayside, he was sent to the far end, away from the Bridge, and next to the escapologist. This was quite fortunate for Mattie, as his new neighbour attracted large crowds as he wriggled out of the chains and ropes in which his audience bound him. Mattie's work was soon noticed and the mats snapped up by the discerning shoppers from south of the river. Arriving home with an empty cart and bulging pockets, Mattie was jubilant.

"Git ya shaal on, Maisie, we're gannin oot to celebrate. Aa've foond the ansa to me problem – Aa'm ganna be the forst proggie mat tycoon in the World!"

After five years, he was receiving orders from all over Europe, and eventually from the Middle East. His prestige gained a great boost, when an order was received from Herrods, the largest department store in Jerusalem. His creation 'The Last Supper', otherwise known as 'Closing Time at the White Horse', was used as the centre-piece of the store's 'Gateshead Week'. This was the occasion when the finest of Gateshead's produce was put on show, as the merchants commenced their drive for exports to the Middle East.

Mattie had set up his factory in Oakwellgate the previous year, in view of the generous grants offered by the Council. His workforce of 50 female proggers worked flat out to meet demand for their standard range. Mattie restricted himself to the specific demands of the wealthy who insisted on individuality. He was working on a mat depicting a whippet running through Team Valley – " 'Monarch o' the Glen' Aa'll caal it" – when a stranger walked into reception.

"Noo there" greeted Mattie.

"Wot cheer" replied the stranger. "Aa'm Peregrine. Aa'm a sorvint o' King Harild."

"Harry King – Aa'd hord 'e'd done weel for 'e'sel. 'E went to school wirriz."

"Aa knaa, 'e telt iz aal aboorrit."

"Aa suppose 'e'll be efta some mats for 'es palace."

"That's reet, but that's noraal … is there somewhere we can taalk?"

"Aye, Aa was just aboot to knock off for me bait. Howay ower the Queen's Heed wirriz; they dee a canny drippin' sanwich."

"Reet, son," began Mattie, using his cuff to wipe the drippin' from his chin, "wot's the botha?"

"Well," whispered the servant, "the gaffa's got spies ower the Channel, an' they reckin the Normans is plannin' to invade England next October."

"Wot can Aa dee aboorrit?"

"Since the spies knaa where the landin's ganna be, Harild 'll be waitin' an' knack them when they try to land. 'E says will ye record the victory for 'im on a greet big mat to hang on the waal 'o their study?"

"Aye, Aa suppose see. How big's the room like?"

"Here's a plan o' the hoose; an' this is the room," he said pointing to a square room with one door and no windows, in the centre of the building, on the plan.

"It says here the room's 9′ high an' 18′ square; Aa'll be able to come up wi' summik. Noo, when's the battle?"

"Sometime next October, the week afore tatie-pickin' week, Aa think."

"An' wheriboots?"

"Pevensey, near Hastings."

"Surely, the illuminations'll be on then?"

"That's reet, so we knaa they'll try nowt at neet. We'd see them miles away."

"Reet – tell Harild Aa'll need a few days notice so Aa can git meesel organised."

"Champion – 'E'll be ower the moon. Their lass's aalwiz pushin' 'im to gan one berra than ivrybody else. 'E thinks this should shut hor up!"

"Ye'll be gannin back the morra mornin, are ye?"

"Aye – does the Queen's dee bed an' breakfist?"

"Nee need for that, Peregrine, ye can stop wirrus at the coast. There's a quiz on at the 'Pheasant' the neet; ye'll enjoy it."

"Aa divvent think see. In the Sooth, we knaa aboot yeez lot bein' scholars and lornin' things, but we cannit schol nowt. It's summik to dee wi the Sooth-North divide, Aa think."

"Aa thowt the King had started to help the depressed areas?"

" 'E did; but it was nee gud. They started sorvin alphabet soup at the soup kitchen to larn wu to write. Most were so clammin' they nivva even saw the letters; an' them as did, aal got wrang cos aal they spelt was swearwords. The King uses me to carry messages cos 'e knaas Aa cannit read them an' spread them aboot. Aa'm not bothad, mind, but it's a pity aboot me sister, Katie."

"Wotsamarra wi hor, like?"

"Well, she's a smashin' story-tella, but she's nivva been to school. If she had, she'd be famiss. She lives near Hastings an' if tha's ganna be botha, she'd be berra off oot the way."

"Why divvent ye send hor here an' she can prog mats during the day an' Aa'll send hor to classes at neet?"

"Soonds canny, that, mind. Aa'll tell hor aal aboorrit when Aa gan yem."

"That's that then. Noo worriboot a game o' darts?"

"Nar, Aa'm nee gud – me eyes is ower bad. Aa even gorroff the coach at Gainsborough cos a thowt the sign said Gaitsit."

"Nivva mind, son. Aa'll gan back to work till ha'past fower, then Aa'll tek ye yem wirriz. Ye can hev a waalk roond the parks and Art Galleries. Ye might even catch the open air Theatre on Windmill Hills. Aa think they're deein 'Look Back in Amble'."

Peregrine stayed overnight at Whitley Bay and returned South to break the news to Harold, and then to Katie.

CHAPTER 2

The Writin' On The Waals!

Katie duly arrived and was set to work on mats with inscriptions such as 'Bless this Hoose' and 'Yem Sweet Yem'. Night classes presented no problem and she sailed through test after test. She did have one difficulty though. Her best writing was only achieved whilst chalking on walls. Her lodgings in Shields were a testing ground for new ideas and plots.

One Monday night in the summer of 1066, Mattie was locking the factory when his father, Albert, rode up to the gates.

"Aa'm ganna need your help, laddie; tha's botha in Shiels."

"Wot's wrang faatha?"

"We got next to nowt delivered the day."

"Faatha, ye knaa tha's aalwiz ganna be weshin lines oot on a Monda...."

"It's nowt to de wi' dryin' claes; it's that progger, Katie; sh's been writin' on the waals an' the carts canna deliver the coal, for aal the wimmin standin' readin' hor stories. The men's aal up in arms, cos tha's nee hoose work gittin done."

"A few waals shudn't caase ower much botha, man."

"A few waals! She's covered ivry waal for fifteen streets! That's wot's wrang!"

"Luk, the next time it rains it'll aal git weshed iway...."

"That's wot Aa thowt, but ivry time it weshes off, she gans streit oot an' writes anotha story. An' aal the wives gan streit oot an' read them. Tha'll be divorce, or worse, before she's done. Blokes is hevvin' to make their own bait, dee the ironin, possin, black-leadin'; while tha' wives is fillin' tha' heeds wi aal this romance! Ye berra git hor sorted oot! And be quick aboorrit."

"Aa'll see worra can dee, faatha, divvent worry!"

She's been writin' on the waals....

Katie, in return for promotion to management, agreed to work only with quill and paper. Her job entailed ensuring that the other proggers completed their work on schedule, so that orders were met. She was given the title Proggeress Chaser, and the keys to a Company bogie.

At the beginning of October, Peregrine returned to the North.

The invasion was imminent. Katie was left in charge of the factory, as Mattie and Peregrine loaded the 35cwt bogie and headed South. Harold was encamped several miles from the coast, and greeted Mattie as he arrived, just west of the A21.

"Noo there, Mattie, wot fettle?"

"Canny man, or shud Aa say 'Sor'?"

"We divvent stand on ceremony here, man; how's business?"

"Champion, wor lass's aalwiz on me back fo' not paintin' the front room, an' the nettie roof's leakin'."

"Aa'm pleased its not just me that's gittin nagged. Noo, Peregrine, Aa want ye to show Mattie the field Aa've hired for the battle. An' when yiv done that, gan an' git some archery practice in – Aa'll need aal the help Aa can git when they come ashore."

Peregrine helped Mattie unload, and set up his gear on the edge of the battlefield. The archers were practising in the next field and Mattie watched as Peregrine joined in.

Soon, everyone was diving for cover. Peregrine was hopeless. Arrows flew in all directions, except towards the target.

Harold arrived and explained that as the battle began he would approach from the left, Northern side of the field so Mattie could get his best side.

"Wotd'ye make o' me archers? Not bad eh?"

"Most o' them luk aal reet, but Aa'm a bit consorned aboot Peregrine, mind. Ye'll hev to watch him. 'E cud hev somebody's eye oot."

Ye'll hev t' watch him – 'E cud hev somebody's eye oot....

The following day, at 8 o'clock, the conflict commenced. Harold started well; too well. Just as he seemed to be gaining the upper hand, the Normans turned and fled to the sea. Lured from his position, Harold advanced. The wily Normans then turned, encircled the Anglo-Saxons and defeated them.

Mattie, having worked through the previous night progging in the background, quickly added the battle scenes. The re-loading of the bogie took longer than expected, as he found space for some local willicks, which he intended to crossbreed with his St. Mary's Island Blueshells. Showing his Press Pass, he was allowed to leave the area and return to the North.

Meanwhile, back in Gateshead, Katie had a problem. A boat load of Persians had arrived in the Tyne, and marched on the factory. Proggie mats had swept through the Middle East following Herrod's 'Gateshead Week' and the Persian market for carpets had slumped. On the principle 'if you can't beat them, join them', they had travelled to Tyneside to retrain.

Their leader Omar Sherif explained "We knaa when t' caal skinchers. Tha's nee point in tryin' to compete wiraal this Westan technology. If yeez'll larn us how t' make proggie mats, we'll work for nowt."

Katie spotted her chance. Free labour, reduced overheads, and expansion without falling into the clutches of Natt West, moneylender of West Street.

"So, yiz wanna make proggie mats. Well, ye knaa wot peeple say: 'Imitation is the sincerest form o' flatulence.' Reet, pitch your tents on the hill above Dunston, sign on at the Club, and be back here the morra mornin' at sivin o'clock."

"Champion" replied Omar, "tha's just one snag: weez aal Muslims – we divvent drink."

"Nivva mind, ye can drink aal ye like – it's nearly aal waata anyway."

The visitors settled on the hilltop, but soon became riven by factional squabbling. The Sunnis moved off to the South, and their village became known as Sunniside. The Shi'ites meanwhile, remained in that we now know as Whickham.

Mattie, on his return, approved of Katie's decision, and formed the visitors into a permanent night shift. Production boomed. Omar was sent overseas as Export Director, to drum up business in the Far East. The mat business was now firmly established and Mattie wrestled with the problems of diversification. Willick-farming as a commercial proposition was still a long way off. Whilst the area was affluent, the populace had few places in which to spend their wealth. And those places which did exist were few and far between. He resolved to create a complex which would concentrate all the major retailers on one site. A field at Earsdon was chosen and he approached Whitley Bay Council for planning permission. The field turned out to be in the Green Belt, and permission was delayed. In the meantime, Mattie, having watched the volume of traffic leaving the Tyne, decided to offer trips around Scandinavia by boat, to his major customers. They became so popular that they had to be offered to the general public.

Jackie, his eldest son, was fresh out of school, and was being groomed for an executive post in the family firm. He was given the particular task of monitoring the progress of the Earsdon planning enquiry. Progress was slow, so Jackie split his time between lobbying the Council and co-operating with Omar on the export drive. Language was no problem as most of the overseas importers spoke Geordie, the universal language of big business.

Omar's success was spectacular. Demand for mats was enormous in the Far East and Africa. Mattie had offered him a profit sharing arrangement, and share-option scheme.

At the quarterly board meeting in early 1069, Omar was offered, and accepted, a place on the board.

"Aa think Aa'll use aal me accumulated wealth ti' invest in some real estate," he announced.

"Wheriboots?" asked Mattie.

"Aa've got me eye on that land up the hill from Deckham."

"Aa thowt the Cooncil had plans t' torn that into an up-market Health Spa?"

"Nar, they've changed their minds; they're ganna build more hooses in Owld Fowld for aal the artists and writers wot canna find lodgins in Bensham. They've been flockin' in from all ower Europe cos they knaa they'll be encouraged ti' express thassels freely."

Omar duly bought his estate up the hill from Deckham, and it's now known as Sherif Hill.

The Persians had not wholly assimilated into the local way of life. Most were prepared, after completing their training, to join the permanent workforce. A dozen or so, however, pined for home and approached Mattie for help. They knew of his boat trips overseas, and suggested that if he could get them as far as Beirut, they would make their own way from there.

"The ownly way Aa cud dee that, wud be if Aa had aboot a hundred more passengers. Otherwise it'd be ower dear. Wor Jackie, mind, reckins that, efta some markit resorch carried oot on the High Street, the money people from Deckham's lukkin fo' summik diffrint. Aa'll send 'im ower to the Evening Chronicle an' git them to advortise a Mediterranean Croose in the next travel supplement. If inuff torn up, yeez can gan for half fare;" offered Mattie.

"Canna argie wi' that, like," said Daud, their spokesman.

"On top o' that, Aal let yiz use my name ower there so ye can start yor oun proggie mat biznizz. It's caaled a franchise; an' aa'l expect to git paid 20 por cent iv owt yez make."

"Yor ower kind, Mr. Hall; we divvent knaa how to thank ye inuff," replied Daud.

The Travel Supplement alternated with the Evening Chronicle Literary Review, so it was a fortnight before the advert brought its overwhelming response. Within a month the Persians were on their way home and the operations of the Marine Division of Hall Enterprises expanded even further.

This did not go unnoticed by the secretary of the local Racing Canary combine. All of the pits in the coalfield had a champion homing canary and races were regularly held from the near-Continent. The Mediterranean would prove a stern test of the elite of these thoroughbreds. The shipping company agreed to transport them free, and liberate them from Majorca, provided that they brought postcards back with them.

The birds were thought to be lost in storms, as their expected time of arrival came and went. Then, late one Friday night, Tadger, representative of Wardley Pit, arrived, bedraggled at the pithead. He was clocked in at 43 days, 7 hours and 15 minutes. The postcard, attached to his leg, was removed and taken to Mattie. The picture showed a night-club in Las Palmas.

"That's not Palma," said Mattie, puzzled. "Must be a misprint."

Turning the card over, the explanation was set out for him.

"Strang winds from the East, Cudn't coin left at Gibraltar. Got blaan reet alang the African coast. Finished up here – amang these islands. Divvent knaa wot they're caaled. Let the bords gan as soon as the wind dropped," read Mattie. The card was from the Captain, Jimmy Cook.

"Aa suppose," decided Mattie, "we shud caal them the Spuggie Islands. Mind iz on to add them onto the advorts for next year's browsha. On seckind thowts, we'll caal them the Canary Islands!"

Harry, Mattie's younger son, like most teenagers of the day, spent long hours listening to the popular music, then fashionable. Maisie did not mind too much, as it gave him a break from his 'A' level studies. Not for him the family business: he wanted to be a poet, and was studying Geordie Language, Geordie Literature, and Green Studies.

He had already fallen out with his grandfather over the question of pollution caused by burning coal. The absence of trees in the Blyth area was caused, according to Harry, by the burning of fossil fuels on Tyneside. The prevailing south-west wind then carried the pollution to Blyth, destroying the trees in the process, with its acid rain. This had created a hole in the ozone layer above Blyth, and as the major coal merchant and exporter in the country, Albert Hall, and his company, 'Global Warming', had to bear the responsibility. It seemed quite a convincing argument. Albert was unmoved and limited his response to one word: 'Bollocks'.

....Tadger arrived bedraggled at the pithead....

Harry's Literature course required him to appraise the works of Georgil the author, Byronclough the poet, and Wilde the playright.

He could recite Georgil's 'Rime of The Whitburn Whipherd', without hesitation. 'Once Upon a Tyne', and 'I Geordius', were his set books and he had no difficulty in mastering them.

The poetry of Byronclough, however, bothered him. The poet, being brought up on Teesside, hadn't quite mastered the Geordie vocabulary. A degree of translation was always necessary, but his tutor spent long hours coaching him.

Wilde's 'The Importance of Being Laid in Windermere' presented no such problems. Although frowned upon by the Establishment, this work had been included in the syllabus by the forward thinking officials in the Education Department. Harry readily identified with Ernest, the hero: abandoned as an infant in a haversack, in the lobby of the Two Bridges Hotel. He hoped to be selected to play Ernest in the 6th form production at Christmas. The previous year he had a large male part in the 'Merry Wives of Windsor Avenue'. It was still the talk of the Upper 6th Girls common room.

CHAPTER 3

Mettre Au Centre

The influence of the Normans was slow in reaching the North East. This was due largely to road-works on the A1 at Wetherby.

The supremacy of Gateshead in matters cultural remained unchallenged. The Latin quarter, at Old Fold, played host to the aspiring artists, poets, and thinkers whose efforts were stifled elsewhere. The artists were led by the gifted Rickleday. Not sure of his preferences for landscapes or portraits, he compromised by painting portscapes. Water colours of Seaham Harbour, Sunderland, Blyth and Tyne Dock were regularly exhibited in the local museums.

One day, whilst lunching on the riverbank at Friars Goose, he was approached by Virgo, the learned astrologer.

"Hiya, Vorgo; does aal this astrologin' caase bad feet?" asked Rickleday.

"Wotcheer, Rick;" replied Virgo. "Ye knaa if Aa divvent plodge ten minutes ivry day, me corns gan mad."

"Aa wish plodgin could sort oot aal my problims," replied Rickleday.

"Wot problims? Ye've got aal the young'ns folleein' yor style; an' aal them scenty gobs from Deckham buyin' yor draains. Wot mair d'ye want, like?"

"Aa divvent knaa: Paintin' duzz'nt satisfy iz nee more. Aa'd rather make things; ye knaa summik useful."

"When's ya borthday?"

"March 19th"

"That makes ye Pisces: so that means ye divvent knaa when ya' weel off'. Ye'll be unda the influence iv Neptune – mebbies ye shud gan into ship buildin'."

"But Vorgo, man, Aa feel like aal these followas is makin' iz oot to be berra than I am."

"That means the presha iv bein' a porsonality is erodin' yor natural creative instincts, an' engenderin' in yor innamost sel' a feelin iv self-doot an' insecurity...."

"Wot's aal tharaboot, Vorgo?"

"Aa divvent knaa – Aa was just practisin' me Horoscope Colum for the Gaitsit Post. Noo – if ye'd been Aquarius Aa'd've telt ye to gan an' invent a way to make waata gan uphill!. An' nivva forget, ye canna make an omlette withoot gittin' egg on ya face!"

"Well, it's time Aa got back to me canvas. Aa'm hevin a try at portrait paintin'."

"Anybody Aa knaa?"

"Aye, Lisa, the Queen o' the Coalfield."

"The Miner Lisa?"

"Aye; an' a reet pest she is an' all. She canna keep hor face streit – aalwiz smorkin."

"Well, just paint wot ye see. It's ownly ganna hang in the Welfare Committee Room."

"Aye, yor reet, Aa cud paint a tash on hor and they'd nivva notice the diffrince."

As the 70's progressed, life on Tyneside continued along its successful way. The Gateshead Festival attracted artists and performers from far and wide, and established itself as the foremost event in the cultural calendar. Harry, now a poet in his own right, performed readings of his own work to packed houses.

Rickleday, struck by the fragrance of a bunch of flowers bought for his sister, Iris's birthday, committed the image to canvas. The painting 'Iris's' formed the centre-piece of his exhibition in the Town Hall. Visitors to the Festival would return overseas to spread the word of Gateshead's artistic supremacy.

On the business front, the old trading families continued to flourish. The descendants of Aristottie, dominated the bakery scene. Relocated to Gosforth to take advantage of the lower wages prevalent in the suburbs, the business was run by Gregory, the high-flying graduate of the Gateshead Council School of Economics. The retail outlets, known as 'Gregs' were located in most neighbourhoods. As profits grew, Gregory could well be grateful for his GCSE qualification.

Mattie Hall's venture into the cruise market breathed new life into the local shipyards. Swan Hunter Boatyard re opened under the new management of a 45th generation Plater. The cruise galleon Ritania, and her larger sister ship, Moritania were designed, built and launched within 12 months. The Mediterranean destinations were extremely popular, requiring larger and larger vessels.

The Vicar's Armament Factory had secured vital export orders. They supplied the Spanish who were fighting the Moors, and the armies of Pope Gregory VII, and Henry IV, the Holy Roman Emperor. They were fighting each other, in Germany.

The production line ran three shifts per day, seven days a week. Armoured personnel bogies, mobile catapults and 'Scout' bogies, were in great demand. Staff were brought in from the South of the river, making regular work for the ferryman, Rowin' Atkinson.

Parson's Heat and Light Works had expanded into telescopes, and attracted clients, both civil and military, to their showpiece observatory on top of Westgate Hill.

Whitley Bay Council was still stalling on planning permission for the Earsdon Shopping Development. Jackie Hall was becoming impatient but, as the philosophical Mattie pointed out to him:

"Gaitsit wasn't built in a day."

Mattie knew from experience that the greater the pressure exerted, the more the Council would stall, in order to demonstrate its independence. So he continued to concentrate on carpets, travel and his family.

It was in March 1080, when William made his first trip to Gateshead. He was to make the official opening of the first Foreign Legion Club in the country. The disused workhouse in Coatsworth Road was refurbished in Norman style to cater for the token force of soldiers posted to the North. It was a favourite posting for the troops, in view of the cosmopolitan sophistication of the locals. The workhouse had closed down some years before for lack of suitably impoverished clients.

William, briefed by his adviser, Dougie Hall, made a courtesy call on Mattie at the Oakwellgate factory. Dougie was a distant relative of Mattie and so was able to persuade him to squeeze William in between two other callers.

"Sorry Aa'm late, Willie," apologised Mattie, "but ye knaa wot them stained glass winda salesmen's like! Cudn't git ridiv'im. Anyway, how'ye keepin?"

"Canny, man," replied William "Aa've been meanin' to tour up here for a lang time, but Aa've had me hands full tryin' to dee summik aboot this Sooth-North divide."

"Ye mean, lornin' thim to coont and read?"

"Aye; an' findin' hooses an' jobs fo' thim...."

"If ye like, Aa'll draa up some plans to revitalise these depressed areas. They might take more notice if it comes from me, like."

"Aye, we can have a bit crack aboorrit the neet."

"Wot's happenin' the neet, like?"

"Tha's a little swarry on at the Legion. We've gorra a late licence – Aa thowt ye might fancy joinin' iz?"

"Aa'm supposed ti be takin' wor lass t' hor mothas – but Aa'll cry off."

"Champion – we're givin' a consat with a French flavour; if ye like ye can girrup an' aal. Aa've hord aal aboot yor singin'."

"That's a lang time since, mind. Aa've nivva sung since Aa got the dust."

"One neet's not ganna hort ye, is it?"

"Na – Aa divvent suppose so. Wot time does it start?"

"Ha'past sivin – but ye berra be in sharp if ye want a gud seat."

"Aal reet, then, Willie, Aa'll see ye."

The Commanding Officer, Beau Lox, put out the 'Hoose Full' sign before seven o'clock, but William had kept Mattie a place near the front. The wine was free, as was the food, which was locked in the games room until the interval. The singers, dancers and jesters put on a good show. None would have come first in the Go as you Please, but they were still good; for Normans. Mattie, duly did a short spot just before closing time. The legionnaires were moved to tears by his rendition of 'Nee Regrets', and cheered by his 'Raindrops Keep Faalin On Me Heed'. He closed with a request from the Chester-le-Street garrison: the haunting Chester Song:

"Chester Song at Twilight.... When the Lights is Low".

As promised, Mattie set off on a tour of the depressed South, in order to advise William.

After years of living off state hand-outs the idea of work did not readily appeal to the populace. A sweep through the Home Counties and the South East allowed Mattie to grasp the enormity of the task.

"It's nee gud us graftin' in the North to subsidise aal these layaboots – they'll hev t' be teached t' help thassels," he reflected.

Using his connections, he arranged for the mine owners from home to explore for coal in Kent, and the ship builders to set up in Portsmouth and Southampton. The artists and writers were encouraged to spend time in the South demonstrating their skills to the locals. At first the reaction was slow, but enough for Mattie to regard his promise to William as having been fulfilled. The skill and expertise which came naturally in the North East continued to filter down to the South. The South-North divide began to narrow, but the South had a lot of catching up to do.

William so enjoyed his trip to the North, that he became a regular visitor. Mattie allowed him to use his caravan on the cliffs a Dawdon. On

The legionnairs were moved to tears....

other occasions he stayed at Whitley Bay with Mattie and Maisie.

On one such visit to Whitley Bay, the plans for the Earsdon development were discussed.

"Aa divvent mean to criticise, like, but, d'ye not think Orsdon's ower far oot o' the way to succeed?" suggested William.

"How d'ye mean?" replied Mattie, surprised.

"If ye luk at the map, Orsdon's on the Northern edge o' the populated area: this shoppin' precinct shud be placed in the middle: as we say in Normandy : 'mettre au centre' "

"Metro Centre?" replied Mattie. "Soonds like a canny name for this development."

"Accordin' to this map, Mattie, Dunston's reet in the middle o' your catchment area."

"Nivva thowt o' that. Dunston eh? Aa'll hev to ask the Cooncil people to make a compulsory porchiss order. The hooses'll need pullin' doon to make way for a development o' this size. The peeple can aal move up the hill to Whickham."

"Aa'm a bit worried aboot the size o' aal this, mind? Where's aal the retailers comin' from?" asked William.

"Aa've aalready got a canny few lined up – Skeets the Apothecary, Gallusses Rack, The Boody Shop, Bensham Home Stores, C&A – ye knaa – Chains and Armour. An' one o' the big 'Dee it Yassel' stores is interested. Aa've even signed up the Jarmin department store Marks & Pfennigs."

"We've invented a new way o' payin' as weel – it's caaled a credit card. Aal ye need dee is sign yor name an' tick the amoont on the bill to prove that ye agree to pay."

"Sort of payin' on tick, ye mean?"

"Aye, there's two cards we accept: one hez crossed axes on it; the other a visor. The poshest peeple'll even hev one o' each."

AXESS
XIV IVCXI
WILLIAM CONQ.
VISOR
CMXI III DCXII
Q. MATILDA

"Surely, that'll tempt peeple to live beyond their means?"

"Ownly if thaa stupit. D'ye remember the cobblers Willis & Hardy?"

"The one's Aa gave the freedom o' Gaitsit for makin' gud skeets forriz?"

"Aye well, they're takin' a shop an aal caaled Freemen Hardy & Willis."

"Well, when it's aal sorted oot, ye can gan ower the Channel an' dee some resorch into holidas forriz."

"Ye mean crooses?"

"Nar – climbin' an' waalkin' holidays in the Moontins. Aa think it cud catch on, if it's set up reet."

The forward-looking, enterprising Gateshead Council quickly granted planning permission for the development. Jackie Hall organised the site clearance, road building and construction work so efficiently that in the autumn of 1086, William came back to carry out the official opening. After the ceremony, William and Mattie returned to Whitley Bay for a break from the celebrations.

"Hev ye seen the results iv aal that resorch we've done aboot England?" said William.

"Ye mean the Domesday Book? Aa knaa thi Chronicle's bowt the rights t' serialise it, but it'll not start till 'Spot the Baal's' won," replied Mattie.

"Accordin' t' the book, ye've still got the proggie mat ye made twenty year ago at Hastings."

"Aye, that's reet; it's in the loft."

"Well, gerrit doon an' let's hev a luk arrit."

The mat was duly dusted off and laid out in the backyard.

"Wor lass'd be ower the moon wi' that. It's hor borthday next week. Howay, then, how much?"

"Sorry, Willie, Aa've grown sortiv attached ti'vit."

"Lukki; if ye lerriz hev it, Aa'll give ye this suit o' chain mail armour."

"Worramaa ganna dee wirra suit o' armour?"

"Well, if ye pull it oot like a pullowa an' stretch it up the coast as far as it'll gan – ye can hev aal that land for yassel."

Mattie pulled at an undarned hole and tugging at the suit, set off up the coast. The chain reached to what is now St. Marys Island. The land so gifted to Mattie is known as 'The Links'.

"Afore Aa shift this mat, ye'll hev to change summik," explained William.

"Wotsamarralike?" asked Mattie.

"Well, Aa knaa, an' ye knaa, that Harild woz bendin' ower fastenin' 'e's basebaal boot when e' woz shot in the behind. Wor lass's a bit aad fashioned. Can ye not hev'im standin' up, wi' the arra in 'e's eye?"

"Aa suppose see; tha's nee point in ye gittin' nagged ower a minor detail like that, is there?"

"There's summik else wor lass's aalwiz on aboot. Hor sista's married to this gadgie who's loaded wi money – an' 'e's built a greet big shally on the coast o' Normandy, where they can gan at weekends. Their bairns have even been capped for the Norman Junior Inshore Plodgin' team. Anyway she's aalwiz on me back aboot hevin a hoose like them. Any ideas?"

"Aye – Aa've got some land just north o' Seahooses, wi ootline plannin' permishin for 150 little hooses or one greet big one. Are ye interested?"

"If it puts one ower on hor Ethel, it'll be champion," replied the King.

"It'll cost ye a few bob mind; the site's got spectacular views ower the sea – ye shud hear Trevor, the estate agent – Aa nearly finish up believin' 'im meesel."

"Lukki, Aa'll tell ye wot Aa'll dee: ye give me the freehowld o' the site, an' Aa'll give ye Jorsey an' Gornsey as a streit swap."

"Hoy in Sark an' Alderney an' it's a deal."

"Done!" agreed the King.

"Aa'll even hoy in the plans for the greet big hoose. That shud save some botha; Aa hear yor laddie's not ower fond o' architects!"

"Aye – yor reet there mind – 'e thinks aal this modern stuff's spoilin' the environment." explained the King.

"Just as well we was browt up afore the environment was discovered."

Over the next few weekends, Mattie and the King set off with half a dozen lads from the Pheasant and set about the construction of the weekend retreat. It soon stood out as a superb example of the self-build technique.

Mattie returned to the South with William, following his invitation to Normandy, to pursue his research into leisure. After a few nights in Caen, they set off for Bordeaux at Mattie's suggestion. He was interested in opening up the market for cruises for the wine-buffs on Tyneside.

The wine growing area impressed Mattie and the tranquillity reminded William of his caravan holidays.

"Aa think we cud caal this place the Dawdogne – it's nearly as gud as the Durham coast." decided William. "When Aa cum here it'll remind iz iv Dawdon."

Mattie acquired some land for the Queen's Head Jolly Boys, who, fed up with Home Brew, wanted to acquire their own vineyards. The land was extensively cultivated, and eventually produced superb wine. It was known as Beaujolais, which is French for Jolly Boys.

They worked their way slowly Eastwards, towards the Mountains which were of particular interest to William. When they reached the Rhône, Bryan, ferryman of note, had knocked off early. There was a social at the club and he was in charge of the music.

"Aa'm ower aad to swim, Mattie," said William.

"Nivver mind, there's a boat ower there – an' two oars," replied Mattie.

It was a Rhône boat.

Safely on the Eastern bank, they headed for the hills. It was autumn now, and the temperature dropped as they climbed.

Unpacking their balaclavas, they set out to identify the potential for the leisure resorts.

"Nee botha wi' buildin' materials, Billy," observed Mattie.

"How d'ye mean like?" replied William.

"Well, luk at aal these trees, man. Pine aren't they?"

"Aye."

"The moontins is covered wi' them. We cud cut thim doon – an' build hooses – pine floors, waals an' roofs – they'll be aal pine hooses. We cud build aal pine villages an' aal, cud'nwe?"

"Gud idea, Mattie; mind iz on afore we gerron the boat, wor lass'll want a souvenir. Worroyi gittin' Maisie?"

"Aa've bowt her a bottle o' porfume an' some boody from Limoges."

"Wor lass's aalready got plenty o' that."

"Well, why divvent ye buy hor a pair o' love-spuggies? Then, ye'll not git wrang for leavin' hor in the hoose."

"Reet, again, Mattie. Where wud Aa be withoot yor wisdom?"

Mattie returned home to find all divisions of the business empire returning record profits. Jackie held the reins and Mattie now 57, took a back seat. Ever since his enforced move to the coast, he had nursed an ambition to return to Gateshead.

In a complicated deal with the Council, he purchased what is now Saltwell Park and built his retirement home in the middle. In return for planning permission, he agreed to landscape the grounds, lay out gardens and permit the public access to this amenity.

In 1087, Mattie was playing draughts in the Park, when a letter arrived, borne by a downcast Peregrine. It read:

> *Dear Uncle Mattie,*
>
> *Me maa says can she take the mat yem to Normandy next week? She hopes ye divvent mind. By the way, me faatha died last week.*
>
> *Hev a nice day,*
>
> *Young Will.*

Peregrine returned the following day with Mattie's reply:

> *Wotcheer Will,*
>
> *Sorry aboot the news. If tha's owt Aa can dee, ye knaa where Aa am. Tell yor maa she can tek the mat ower the waater. But rememba, it'll need dry cleanin' ivry fower years. Divvent fogget yor leek-growin' correspondence course. Aa'm lukkin forwad to presentin' yor diploma at the Tech College, next year.*
>
> *Gan canny,*
>
> *Uncle Mattie.*

Matilda, Mrs. The Conqueror, duly returned to Normandy, and with her went Doug Hall. He had promised William that he would look after her and true to his word, he took a correspondence course in Royalty.

In 1090, after he had qualified, he married the Queen and became 'King Dougie the Forst', the most powerful man in France. The family moved to a detached chateau at 'Colombey les deux Eglises'. One of his descendants was to become President many centuries later.

The proggie mat was presented to the Town of Bayeux and it hangs there to this day, as testimony to Geordie craftsmanship and ingenuity.

Mattie deferred retirement to help look after the business. The King had left plans for an Embassy on the Coast Road and Mattie used his influence with the Planning Department to ensure planning permission was not delayed. The magnificent structure soon dominated the eastern approaches to Newcastle. Such was its scale, that the diplomats used only a small proportion of its cavernous interior.

Mattie rented part of the ground floor to experiment with a pet theory. The local rhubarb industry was still dominant in the World Rhubarb Council. Mattie, however, still felt that the leaves, normally discarded, could be put to better use. The Marketing Board delivered a ton of leaves to the back door of the Embassy, free of charge.

After months of tests involving drying and shredding the leaves, the correct consistency was achieved. Wrapping the mixture into a rolled-up 'Spot the Ball' entry, he ignited on end and sucking the other end, inhaled the rhubarb smoke. The relaxant effect was immediate. Mattie knew instinctively that a major discovery had been made. The product, named 'Will's Embassy', after its birthplace, swept the country, as Mattie's carpets had previously.

The other major building under construction at the time was taking shape a little further North. The King, wishing to keep track of his subjects, had set up the Domesday Security Service, to be based at Longbenton. It was to become a major employer in the years which followed.

Meanwhile at the Metro Centre, Marks had fallen out with his partner, Pfennigs, over plans to open another store in Northumberland Street. Pfennigs decided to go it alone and took premises near the junction with Blackett Street. He was very successful. Marks took in a new partner and in view of Pfennigs' success, opened another store further up Northumberland Street.

South of the river, the Council had problems with a pressure group which campaigned for the 'greening' of the North Team Valley. They wished to evict the businesses which had established themselves on the banks of the river. 'Hands of wor TV' signs appeared overnight on the hoardings in Bensham Road.

It was decided, after much agitation, to offer land, free of rates, to the industrialists to encourage them to move south of Lobley Hill Road. This 'Enterprise Zone' attracted most of the businesses onto the newly formed Estate. The soft drinks factory 'Norwood Coke Works' was compulsorily purchased and demolished.

A new business, specialising in dug-out canoes for export, 'Hew Wood', took the first site; and was followed closely by 'Smiths Delivery Bogies'; and the mint factory owned by the French transvestite 'De La Rue'.

The North Team Valley was then handed over to the Parks Department and intensive reclamation carried out. In view of the cosmopolitan nature of the town, travellers often returned from overseas with examples of exotic flora. These were kept under glass at the Nurseries at the top of Lobley Hill Bank. The Parks Department decided to put them on display to the general public. Elaborate arrangements were created throughout the Area of Outstanding Natural Beauty, which was the Council's official designation of the site.

The centre-piece of the display was the prize winning collection of 85 varieties of leek exhibited by the Council leader. Being a descendant of the Gateshead Scholar, Georgil, he explained that the Pyramid, which housed the collection, was an old Egyptian word for 'Bait Cabin'.

The Gateshead National Allotment Festival was officially opened on May 18th, 1090. The ceremony was performed by King William II, before an invited audience, including councillors, club chairmen and the press. The Chronicle reporter, Peter, fairly raced back to Pudding Chare to submit his copy of the event.

A large banquet was held later at the 'Two Bridges Hotel'. The best of French and local cuisine were combined to create such delicacies as black-pudding vol-au-vents, and willicks mornay. These comprised of freshly picked Cullercoats willicks in a melted Camembert. The pudding-bogie itself was a sight for sore eyes. Rhubarb was widely used in mousses, meringue pies and gateaux.

Massive crowds travelled from far and wide to witness this spectacle. Gate receipts exceeded all expectations, and thought was even given by the Council to reducing the level of domestic poll tax. The profits were, however, invested in further expansion of the Technical College and the offer to deprived children in depressed Guildford, of scholarships. It was all part of the twinning arrangement.

Needless to say, the rare and exotic plants on display tempted visitors to take home souvenirs. Site security was in the capable hands of Hender, who patrolled the site in his Panda-bogie. During the five months of the Festival, only five arrests were made and these were for being drunk in charge of a bogie. Visitors frequently under estimated the power of the specially brewed Festive-Ale, which was a bit like Exhibition.

Pilfering was, therefore, non-existent, and Hender was subsequently honoured for his services to the town. He was awarded an O.G.E. (Order of the Gateshead Empire).

The gardens remained an asset to the town, and provided an oasis of calm in the midst of, what was then, as now, a vibrant, expanding Tyneside.

CHAPTER 4

Yagannin Streits!

The cruise schedules became crowded, as the locals grew more wealthy. Demand soared and new vessels were commissioned, for delivery in the 90's.

"Wot we need," decided Jackie, "is a greet big boat that'll gan berra than aal the others; carry more toorists, and make more money."

Swan Hunter came up with the record-breaking 'Ganberra', equipped with all the latest 'State of the Ark' technology.

Captains returning from the Mediterranean reported friction in several ports of call. Cruise liners were often greeted by protesters chanting "Geordies gan yem", "Doon wi Gaitsit", and "Geordie Imperialists" (after the little round mints that they gave to the local children). Whilst there was always some resentment at the apparent wealth of the tourists, the new problems were of deeper significance.

"Spot o' botha in Torkey, Jackie," reported Captain Blyth after the 1093 trip.

"Aa thowt it woz aalwiz quiet doon there – just like Exeter," replied Jackie.

"Torkey, man, not Torquay!" corrected Blyth.

"Well why didn'ye say so," laughed Jackie.

"Anyway, the Cooncil's doubled the landin' fees...."

"Worriboot the passage and staircase?" laughed Jackie.

"Howay, man, this is serious. It's even warse in Syria. Fassad, the Cooncil Chairman's caasin trouble...."

"'E's not the real leader, Shay, 'e's ownly a front man."

"Aa divvent care. Between them, the Torks and Syrians is ganna affect next year's accoonts – the profit margins'll aal be doon. Mark my wards – ye berra cross the far end o' the Med oot o' the itineraries," warned Shay.

"Noo ya taalkin – faalin profits eh? Aa'll send wor Harry ower next year on a fact-findin' mishin. If the Med's oot, we'd berra find some new destinashins, hadn't we?"

"Worriboot coinin reet, insteed o' left doon the Channel?" ventured Shay.

"Nee demand for holidiz in Ireland, man."

"Nar, not Ireland; fortha West."

"Ye might be full o' advencha, Shay, but the public's not ready for nowt like that. Mind, if ye want to gan yassel an' find oot, ye can hev time off work. Aa'll tell ye wot: ye gan West, while wor young'un gans East, an' we can decide on strategy when ye both get back."

It was November 1094, when Shay returned. Months of sailing had produced no landfall and only a handful of icebergs.

"Luks like ye wor reet, Jackie. Nee money to be made oot there. How'd Harry gan on?"

"Aa divvent knaa, Shay; Aa've hord nowt since the Palma canary came in. Aa'm gittin a bit worried."

"Aa telt ye there'd be botha, didn't Aa?"

"Aye, Shay: Aa shud've listened to ye: trouble is the King's sister's on the croose; educashinal trip, ye knaa. 'E's due here next Thorsday to pick hor up."

Thursday arrived. The boat didn't.

"Aa'm not ower happy aboot this mind, Jackie?" complained Will. "Wor-royi ganna dee aboorrit?"

"Leave it ower the weekend – if Aa've hord nowt by Monda, Aa'll put me contingency plan into action." promised Jackie.

He was straightening a line of shopping trolleys in the Metro Centre when a bogie screeched to a halt beside him. It was driven by Ada, ace reporter of the Sunderland Echo. It was Saturday lunchtime.

"Wotcheer Ada, worro'yee deein ower here?" asked Jackie, puzzled.

"Noo there, Jackie: Aa'm ifraid Aa've got bad news," she explained. "Aa'm just back from the Middle East: Aa woz coverin' an Orange March in Jaffa, when Aa catched a glimpse o' yor Harry – 'E telt iz they'd been hijacked an' forced to sail to the Holy Land. They were gannin to be held hostage in Jerusalem."

"Hostages? Wot for?"

"The Cooncil wants pormishin for their crooses to hev equal access to the Tyne and Wear."

"If they'd asked, they wud've got pormishin wi nee botha. But we canna just let them gerraway wi their impittince. Where'd aal this happen?"

"Between the coast an' the Island o' Yagannin."

"Yagannin Streits!"

"Honest, that's wot 'e said; anyway gis a quote; it'll probbly make the neet's Echo," asked Ada.

"Aal reet: ye can quote iz 'These forrinaz hevvint hord the last o' this!' Come back ower on Monda and Aa'll hev inutha story for ye."

Jackie was in his office at 9 o'clock sharp on the Monday morning.

"Any news?" asked Will on his arrival.

"Aye, Aa've got news aal reet, but haad on – Aa've got somebody comin' ower to give a hand."

Ada arrived, followed quickly by Shay.

"Hiya, Ada; that woz a good'un ye wrote aboot Tripoli last July; did ye not git hort?" Will asked.

"Nar – its aal part o' the job – Aa divvent worry aboorrit," she shrugged.

Ada then explained the encounter with Harry, in Jaffa, and that all the passengers seemed well. Will agreed that permission would have been a formality had it been requested. However, the use of force could not go unanswered.

"Yor reet, Jackie, we shud gan ower an' sort thim aal oot." agreed Will.

"Reet – Aa'll supply the boats, ye supply the sowljers, an' - we'll send an expedishin to gan an' bring ivrybody back" suggested Jackie.

"Soonds aal reet ti me like," agreed Will.

"An' we'll caal it Croose Aid," decided Jackie.

A detailed plan was drawn up, with nothing left to chance. The flagship of the fleet, the Ganberra, was withdrawn from service on the Scandinavian run and made ready. It would serve as HQ for the King and Jackie, and the senior ranks in the Legion. The older vessels were gathered off the mouth of the Tyne, ready to convey the fighting men. Further recruits would be picked up at Barcelona, Marseilles and Naples.

The problem of the wives left behind continued to cause concern. In order to protect them from the unwanted attentions of the amorous conscientious objectors who remained, it was decided to requisition the Penshaw Cartel for the duration of the expedition. In view of its elevated position, it was relatively easy to protect. The local farmer, Lambton, also offered his unique security force, the fearsome megaworm. It would be allowed to roam the grounds freely, in order to deter uninvited guests.

On the morning of pancake Tuesday in 1095, tearful farewells were bade, as the massed cazoos of the Percy Main Academy of Music, wailed the totally inappropriate "Doo doo doo-doo doo-doo doo-doo doo-doo-doo (We're aal gannin on a summa holida)." The fleet formed up, and with Ganberra at its head, headed South.

The expedition force ploughed on South and then East, past cheering crowds at Gibraltar. Volunteers were taken on board in Barcelona, and then in Marseilles. The Ganberra provided its normal standard of luxury and entertainment to the top brass. The nightly cabaret was attended by almost the entire complement of the vessel. The veteran tenor Grampa Varotti nightly displayed the range which made him the highest

On the morning of Pancake Tuesday in 1095, tearful farewells were bade....

paid performer employed by Jackie; after the bingo caller, that is. Unfortunately, somewhere between Sicily and Calabria he lost his voice. The mood became ugly at his non-appearance. Mutiny was only just avoided when Jackie discovered an able substitute, Placebo Domingo. As Grampa Varotti recovered, intense rivalry was created between the two. Eventually, the bingo was jettisoned, to give each performer equal time before their learned fellow travellers.

It was the Thursday in Race Week, when the fleet dropped anchor off Palestine. The King called a council of war in the ballroom.

"Reet lads," he began, "Aa knaa ye'd aal ratha be on the Hoppins wi' the bairns, but this is a principle we're fightin' aboot. Noo, me an' Jackie've sorted oot some tactics. Forst, in classic Norman fashion, we'll land ower a broad front on fower main beaches, aroond Jaffa.

Second, we'll aal spread oot, an' convorge on Jerusalem from the North, West and Sooth.

Thord, based on me fatha's tactics at Hastin's, the force from the West, led by me will make on its runnin' away. When the enemy comes oot to chase, the North contingent, led by me sorvint Oliver, will surroond aal o' them while, Jackie, in charge o' the Sooth, can enter Jerusalem an' free the hostages.

Reet? Noo, Aa'm sure ye knaa that the Northumberland Plate's run on Saturda, so we'll land then, on 'P' Day. The plan's caaled 'Operashin Owerboard'. Noo, if anybody wants a bet on the Plate, Ladbroke, the porser's, runnin' a book."

The officers returned to their vessels, and outlined the plan to the men. The following day was spent preparing for the conflict and writing letters home. It was a heavy laden flock of canaries which headed for Cyprus on the first leg on the Friday night.

At first light on 'P' Day, a thick mist descended which was to have a crucial bearing on the landing. The King agreed with Jackie that the landing be delayed until visibility improved. Around midday the mist disappeared leaving a clear view of totally deserted beaches.

The bogie landing craft nosed towards the shore, in what was to be the first amphibious assault in history. They landed unopposed and swiftly advanced inland.

"Aa divvent like the luk o' this mind," said Jackie, uneasily. "It's ower easy – mebbies its a trap or summik."

"Haad on, man," replied Shay, "isn't it Cup Final day?"

"Aa cudn't say for sortin...."

"Why, aye, man, Jaffa's playin' Hebron in Jerusalem. They'll aal hev went to the match."

Progress was made much quicker than expected. Oliver, and his contingent in the North, were so ahead of schedule that they allowed themselves a stop for ice cream, at Wall's of Jericho.

Jackie, likewise encountered the deserted streets of Hebron with some relief. Descended from the settlers from Hebburn, the townspeople were renowned for their liking for a good fight.

Will, as planned, approached in strength up to the suburbs. At 5 o'clock, the streets were still quiet. The final had gone to extra-time. Perfectly positioned, his master cazooist, Laverick, was ordered to announce their presence.

"Doo doo doo doo doo doo doo doo (Oh when the Saints go marchin' in)" had an electrifying effect on the defenders.

As expected they were quickly into battle formation, and confronting the aggressors. At 5.30, Will turned tail and fled. The defenders followed and were immediately cut off by Oliver's men. Jackie had the simple task of locating and liberating the hostages.

They had been held captive for almost two years, inspite of which Harry and the King's sister, were unharmed. Harry rushed forward to embrace his liberator.

"Wotcheer, Harry; are ye aal reet?" greeted Jackie.

"Nivva mind aboot me, Jackie, wot won the Plate?"

....a stop for ice cream at Wall's of Jericho....

By nightfall, the hostages were safely aboard 'Ganberra' which was to sail on the morning tide. The rescue of the hostages completed the first objective of Cruise Aid. The second task, to pacify the natives, was to take another four years. Will entrusted the task to Beau Lox and a large contingent of the Legion.

The piers at the mouth of the Tyne were packed with cheering crowds as 'Ganberra' made her triumphal entrance into the river.

"She's surroonded by a fleet o' smaall boats" wrote Ada as she completed her report on the success of the expedition.

"It's like an armada," explained Placebo.

"Wots one o' them, like?" queried Ada.

"Armada? It's Spanish for 'a canny few'," replied the singer. He had been lured back to Tyneside in the hope of finding work with the Chapel House Amateur Operatic Society.

The returning heroes were swiftly transferred to Penshaw to be reunited with their loved ones, and their wives. The watch-worm had proved an effective deterrent, and no suitor had managed to approach within one hundred yards of the Cartel. Unfortunately, the celebrations were marred when the worm met an ill timed death. Having consumed eight pails of beer, he strayed onto the main road and was run over by a heavy goods bogie.

"Aa think," declared Jackie, "that, withoot the worm, we mightn't hev been able to hev such a successful expedition. So, Aa feel its ownly fair that we honour it's memory in some way – a monument or summik." Everyone agreed.

In a matter of weeks, most Councils in the area had erected monuments in their High Streets. They were known as Worm Memorials.

Having consumed ....

ODE TO THE BANKS

by

HARRY HALL

As a bairn Aa'd watch the mornin mist
Rise ower yonda bank,
And sit bewitch'd as sunlight kissed,
The bogies on the Taxi rank.

And then appeared the roofs and towers
Fortha from the Quay,
So Aa wud sit, and sit for hours,
Dying for a tea.

A boat tied up at Hillgate borth,
Back from forrin parts,
A spuggy fluttered doon t' orth
And plodged amang the clarts.

Alang the shore to left and reet,
The lads fished from the steps
And lasses from the High Street,
Played stot the baal and keps.

The sun sank ower Wesgit Hill,
The shadows faallin fast,
And havin nee more time to kill,
Aa'd leave the banks at last.

A spuggy fluttered doon t' orth
And plodged amang the clarts....

GAN NORTH YOUNG MAN
by
BYRONCLOUGH: POET.

Noo divvent sit withoot a plan,
To find yassel a job o' work,
Ye knaa there's nen to find in York,
So Aa wud say, gan North, Young Man.

Aa'm sortin ye've hord aal aboot
Them high piece work rates up there
An' aal them lassies, sweet an' fair,
So, away and take the A1 route.

An' when ye reach the busy Tyne,
An' aal them fancy places,
Ye'll soon find oot the livins fine,
Wi aal them smilin faces,
There'll be nee time to sit and pine,
So gan yem noo and pack your cases.

'JAILER BRING IZ WAATER' 'PLEASE RELEASE IZ'

by

HARRY HALL

The liner torned Sooth in mid – 94,
And heeded for Palestine's silver shore.
Ten miles to gan and sun scorchin doon
Aa sit on the fore-deck and think o' the Toon.

The boat tied up in the aad port o' Jaffa,
Two dockers embarked, alang wi' thor gaffer.
The Captain, unhappy at wot 'e' woz telt,
Went for the sword, wot hung from his belt.

They led him away and suroonded the boat,
Wi' sowljers and sailors in owt that cud float.
Then we woz telt we wor aal forrin spies,
And trooped off the liner, wi' scarves on wor eyes.

Noo, we're in jail and tied up wi' chains,
And git nowt to drink, unless we hev rains.
It's gittin' that hot, Aa pray for monsoon,
And sit on the top bunk and think o' the Toon.

It's nice to sail to forrin parts
And waatchin the prisonaz shovellin clarts,
Was not wot we'd planned at Gaitsit quay
But noo, through the bars, it's all Aa can see.

We aal sing the songs we lornt in school,
And taalk aboot games, and hoops we cud bool,
But the youn'uns is worried and fear for their fate
And we laugh and wonda what horse won the Plate.

But laughin's aalwiz froond upon
And 'Whole lorra sheikhin gannin on'
Interrupted on Juke Box Jewry,
Makes the jailer swear wi fury.

Ootside Aa see an aaful commoshin
Wi sowljers, come from ower the ocean,
Wor Jackie's amang them, oot in the yard
And wavin' 'e's sword he chases the guard.

And so, hevin sat for a year in this jail
We're free to gan yem, and drink beer by the pail
So back on the top deck, Aa look at the Moon,
And coontin me blessins, Aa think o' the Toon.

NOW AVAILABLE DIRECT FROM:

WARD ENNIS PUBLICATIONS
3 EARSDON ROAD
WEST MONKSEATON
WHITLEY BAY
TYNE & WEAR NE25 9SX

Please forward ____________ copy/copies of:

ONCE UPON A TYNE

at £3.00 per copy (including P&P).
I enclose my Cheque/Postal Order for £_____:__
Please send the above copy/copies to:

M ____

Address ___________________________________

____

____

______________________Post Code:__________

NEED ANOTHER COPY?

IF YOU HAVE DIFFICULTY THEN CONTACT:

WARD ENNIS PUBLICATIONS
3 EARSDON ROAD
WEST MONKSEATON
WHITLEY BAY
TYNE & WEAR NE25 9SX

Please forward ____________ copy/copies of:

GATESHEAD REVISITED

at £3.00 per copy (including P&P).
I enclose my Cheque/Postal Order for £_____:__
Please send the above copy/copies to:

M____

Address____

____

____

________________________Post Code:__________